CELEBRITY QUIZZES

D1420340

FFirst published in 2002 by Miles Kelly Publishing Ltd,
Bardfield Centre, Great Bardfield, Essex, CM7 4SL

This edition printed 2002

ISBN 1-84236-131-7

2 4 6 8 10 9 7 5 3

Project Manager: Ian Paulyn
Assistant: Lisa Clayden
Design: Clare Sleven

Contact us by email: info@mileskelly.net
Website: www.mileskelly.net

Printed in India

CELEBRITY QUIZZES

by
Christopher Rigby

Miles
Kelly
PUBLISHING

About the Author

Born in Blackburn, Lancashire in 1960, Christopher Rigby
has been compiling and presenting pub quizzes for the past
15 years. When he is not adding to his material for quizzes,
Christopher works in the car industry. He is married to
Clare – they have two teenage daughters, Hollie and Ashley
and share their home with two demented dogs called Vespa
and Bailey. A keen Manchester United fan Christopher lists
his heroes as George Best and Homer Simpson.

CELEBRITY QUIZZES EXPLAINED

In my many years as a pub quiz compiler I have found that the inclusion of a number of celebrity quizzes has proved to be a popular addition to the night's festivities.

Each quiz provides a profile of a famous person in the form of five clues, which are supposed to get easier as the points value reduces.

The 1 point clue will hopefully give away the indentity. Below is an example:

5 POINT CLUE This famous man was born in 1927 and left school to work down the coal mines.

4 POINT CLUE In 1990 he received a knighthood.

3 POINT CLUE In 1997 he underwent a quadruple heart bypass operation despite the fact that he had run in over 200 marathons.

2 POINT CLUE He presented Top of the Pops for over 20 years.

1 POINT CLUE This DJ hosted 'Jim'll Fix It' on TV.

ANSWER = Sir Jimmy Saville

QUIZ ONE

....

5 POINT CLUE A famous name in the world of show-business, he was born in 1942. By the time he had reached his 12th birthday he was starring in films made by the Children's Film Foundation.

4 POINT CLUE He left a Shakespeare touring company to co-star with John Lennon and Roy Kinnear in the film *How I Won The War*.

3 POINT CLUE He also starred in the Hollywood musical *Hello Dolly* but he will be best remembered for one particular comedy role that he played on British TV.

2 POINT CLUE On the stage he has played Billy Liar, the Phantom of the Opera and P T Barnum.

1 POINT CLUE He played Frank Spencer in *Some Mothers Do 'Ave 'Em*.

ANSWER
MICHAEL CRAWFORD

QUIZ TWO

5 POINT CLUE This mystery man, famous in the world of sport, was born in June 1939. After he retired he became a TV commentator on the sport for which he is famous.

4 POINT CLUE He was awarded the OBE in 1972 and one year later he retired as a world champion.

3 POINT CLUE He was born in Scotland and in 1973 he was voted BBC Sports Personality of the Year.

2 POINT CLUE He has represented Great Britain in the Olympic games at clay pigeon shooting.

1 POINT CLUE In 1969, 1971 and 1973 he was the Grand Prix World Motor Racing Champion.

ANSWER
JACKIE STEWART

QUIZ THREE

5 POINT CLUE Famous in the world of music, he was born in Reading in 1953. In 1990 he released a single that failed to chart despite being extensively used in a TV advert for Nurofen painkillers.

4 POINT CLUE He recorded his first album in 1968 with his sister. That album was entitled *Children Of The Sun*.

3 POINT CLUE In 1975 he won his first Grammy Award and in 1981 he became only the first rock musician after Paul McCartney to be entered into the UK edition of *Who's Who*.

2 POINT CLUE In 1980 he had a Top 20 hit with his adaptation of the *Blue Peter* TV theme.

1 POINT CLUE His album *Tubular Bells* was used for the theme for the film *The Exorcist*.

ANSWER
MIKE OLDFIELD

QUIZ FOUR

5 POINT CLUE This mystery actress was born in 1949 and in 1973 she appeared in a film called *The Paper Chase*.

4 POINT CLUE In the film *Nighthawks* she provided the romantic interest for Sylvester Stallone.

3 POINT CLUE She shares her surname with a famous composer and an actor who died in the film *The Towering Inferno*.

2 POINT CLUE On TV she had starring roles in the dramas *Princess Daisy* and *Scruples*.

1 POINT CLUE In her most famous role she was rebuilt as the *Bionic Woman*.

ANSWER
LINDSAY WAGNER

QUIZ FIVE

5 POINT CLUE This famous man was born in London in October 1923. After serving in the Army during World War II he studied law at Oxford University where he was elected President of the Union.

4 POINT CLUE After being called to the Bar in 1952 he practised law for a year and then left to join the BBC as a radio talk-show producer.

3 POINT CLUE In September 1955 he defected to ITV and along with Christopher Chataway he became one of ITV's first newsreaders.

2 POINT CLUE In 1959 he stood as a Liberal candidate at the General Election and in 1981 he received a knighthood.

I POINT CLUE This former presenter of the current affairs TV show *Question Time* won several Bow Tie Wearer of the Year Awards during his lifetime.

ANSWER
SIR ROBIN DAY

QUIZ SIX

5 POINT CLUE This famous lady was born in London in 1965. When she was just 22 years old she wrote a play called *Mr Thomas*. In 1991 she won a *Time Out* Award for directing that play at a London theatre.

4 POINT CLUE In 1982 while still attending drama school she appeared in her first film role, a controversial drama called *Scrubbers* set in a girls' borstal.

3 POINT CLUE On TV she played a hairdresser in the drama series *Common As Muck* and on film she played Mary Tudor in the award-winning film *Elizabeth*.

2 POINT CLUE In 1997 she won a Best Actress Award at the Cannes Film Festival for her role in the film *Nil By Mouth*.

1 POINT CLUE Alongside Harry Enfield she has played Waynetta Slob and Perry the Teenager.

ANSWER
KATHY BURKE

QUIZ SEVEN

5 POINT CLUE This mystery singer was born in Illinois in 1953 and in 1986 she performed a duet with David Bowie which featured on the soundtrack for the film *Labyrinth*.

4 POINT CLUE In 1969 she joined a group called Shades of Black as lead vocalist and in 1980 she released a solo album called *Naughty*.

3 POINT CLUE The first name of her stage name when translated into English means 'fire'. In 1984 she topped the UK singles charts with a song written by Prince.

2 POINT CLUE Her real name is Yvette Marie Stevens.

1 POINT CLUE Her hit records include 'I Feel For You' and 'I'm Every Woman'.

ANSWER
CHAKA KHAN

QUIZ EIGHT

5 POINT CLUE This famous sportsman was born on Valentine's Day in 1951 and made his full international debut for England in 1972.

4 POINT CLUE He won his last England cap in 1982 and in 1976 he was voted Footballer of the Year.

3 POINT CLUE. He began his football league career at lowly Scunthorpe United but by 1979 he had won his second European Footballer of the Year Award.

2 POINT CLUE He ended his playing career at St James's Park and in 1979 he had a Top 40 hit record with a song called 'Head Over Heels In Love'.

1 POINT CLUE He left the hot seat at Fulham FC to become the manager of the England football team.

ANSWER
KEVIN KEEGAN

QUIZ NINE

....

5 POINT CLUE This mystery man died from cancer in August 1972 and during World War II he served in the RAF teaching navigation and low-level flying.

4 POINT CLUE Between the World Wars he emigrated with his family to New Zealand where he became a very successful estate agent before returning to England in 1926.

3 POINT CLUE His surname can be found in West Sussex.

2 POINT CLUE In 1967 he was knighted by the Queen at Greenwich.

I POINT CLUE He circumnavigated the globe in a boat called *Gypsy Moth*.

QUIZ TEN

5 POINT CLUE This famous American was born in Missouri in 1847 and when he was just three years old his father, a Baptist minister, passed away.

4 POINT CLUE At the age of 15 he joined a group of southern guerillas and fought against the Unionists in the American Civil War.

3 POINT CLUE After the war he turned to a life of crime and died a violent death in 1882. He was played on film by Tyrone Power in 1939.

2 POINT CLUE In 1990 he was the subject of a hit record by Cher.

I POINT CLUE He was shot and killed by Bob Ford for a $10,000 reward and he led a gang of outlaws with his brother Frank.

ANSWER
JESSE JAMES

QUIZ ONE

....

5 POINT CLUE This famous lady was born in 1940 and attended Oxford University. She was awarded the OBE in 1990 and has won several TV Personality of the Year Awards.

4 POINT CLUE In 1988 Billy Cotton offered her the post of Controller of the BBC but she turned it down.

3 POINT CLUE After leaving university she joined the BBC as a studio manager before becoming a member of the cast in the BBC consumer comedy programme *Braden's Week*.

2 POINT CLUE In 1977 she married Desmond Wilcox.

1 POINT CLUE On TV she has presented *Hearts of Gold* and *That's Life*.

ANSWER
ESTHER RANTZEN

QUIZ TWO

5 POINT CLUE This famous actor was born in 1948 and when he was just 13 years old he made his big-screen debut in a film called *Pirates of Blood River*.

4 POINT CLUE Other films include *Up The Junction*, *Man In The Wilderness* and *The Belstone Fox*. He will probably be best remembered for his TV work and whilst he was still a teenager he appeared in the 1960s TV series *Fair Exchange*.

3 POINT CLUE He battled against the forces of evil in the shape of Christopher Lee in the film *Scars Of Dracula*. In 1980 he enjoyed a No. 3 hit single with a TV theme song.

2 POINT CLUE Whilst he was still a schoolboy he played the schoolboy *Just William*. He married and divorced the actress Rula Lenska.

1 POINT CLUE He played Terry McCann, the minder of Arthur Daley.

ANSWER
DENNIS WATERMAN

QUIZ THREE

5 POINT CLUE This famous singer was born in 1932 and early in his show-business career he performed as a jazz guitarist. His mother was captured and imprisoned by the Gestapo.

4 POINT CLUE In 1963 he married an Olympic skiing champion after a romance with Bridget Bardot fizzled out.

3 POINT CLUE At the age of 68 he took the male lead in the West End stage production of the musical *Chicago*.

2 POINT CLUE In the year 2000 he was impersonated on the TV show *Stars In Their Eyes* by David Ginola.

1 POINT CLUE The only UK hit in the 20th century for this French heart-throb was 'Raindrops Keep Falling On My Head'.

ANSWER
SACHA DISTEL

QUIZ FOUR

5 POINT CLUE This famous man was born in Yorkshire in March 1934. After serving in the RAF he joined drama school and made his stage debut as a clown in a Cyril Fletcher pantomime.

4 POINT CLUE He is one of the most famous faces on British TV and has written several books, the first of which was entitled *The Flight Of The Magic Clog*.

3 POINT CLUE In the 1980s he presented Country Calendar for Yorkshire TV and hosted *The Saturday Show* for the ITV breakfast service.

2 POINT CLUE His voice can be heard in several TV adverts including Andrex toilet rolls, and he appeared in the flesh in an advert for Everest double glazing.

I POINT CLUE He was often heard shouting 'Get down Shep' on *Blue Peter*.

ANSWER
JOHN NOAKES

QUIZ FIVE

5 POINT CLUE This famous actor was born during World War II and was once jailed for two years for conspiracy to intimidate in picket-line violence.

4 POINT CLUE Films he has appeared in include *Butterfly Kiss*, *Raining Stones* and *Riff Raff*.

3 POINT CLUE In the award-winning TV series *Cracker* he played DCI Wise.

2 POINT CLUE In the soap opera *Brookside* he played Bobby Grant.

1 POINT CLUE He has won a host of awards for his role of Jim Royle in the comedy series *The Royle Family*.

ANSWER
RICKY TOMLINSON

QUIZ SIX

5 POINT CLUE This famous singer was born in March 1968 and had her first Top 10 hit in the UK in 1992.

4 POINT CLUE She has sung duets with Peabo Bryson, Barbra Streisand and R. Kelly.

3 POINT CLUE Her hit records include 'Treat Her Like A Lady', 'Misled', 'Love Can Move Mountains' and 'I'm Your Angel'.

2 POINT CLUE She was born in Quebec and in 1988 she represented Switzerland in the Eurovision Song Contest.

1 POINT CLUE She enjoyed a No. 1 smash all over the world in 1998 with the theme song from *Titanic*.

ANSWER
CELINE DION

QUIZ SEVEN

5 POINT CLUE This famous man was born in 1874 and when he was just 19 years old he got married to a young woman that he had accidentally spilt acid over.

4 POINT CLUE He was the son of a Hungarian Jewish Rabbi, and he died in 1926.

3 POINT CLUE In 1953 he was played on film by Tony Curtis.

2 POINT CLUE His real name was Ehrich Weiss and he died after being punched in the stomach.

I POINT CLUE He was probably the most famous escapologist of all time.

ANSWER
HARRY HOUDINI

QUIZ EIGHT

5 POINT CLUE This famous man was born in Cheltenham in 1942 and when he was a child his family emigrated to New Zealand. He returned to Cheltenham in 1964 after finishing a hairdressing apprenticeship.

4 POINT CLUE Despite being completely bald in later years, he toured in the rock stage show of *Hair*.

3 POINT CLUE His real name is Richard Smith and he played the villain in the film *Spice Girls The Movie*.

2 POINT CLUE He is the creator of *The Rocky Horror Picture Show*.

1 POINT CLUE For several years he presented the TV game show *The Crystal Maze*.

ANSWER
RICHARD O'BRIEN

QUIZ NINE

5 POINT CLUE This mystery lady famous in the world of show-business released her debut album in 1999, which topped the UK album charts.

4 POINT CLUE In the year 2000 she released her autobiography which was entitled *Follow Your Dreams*.

3 POINT CLUE She was born in Yorkshire and she worked on the *Galaxy*.

2 POINT CLUE On TV she presented a show for singing hopefuls called *Star For A Night*.

1 POINT CLUE She became an overnight star after appearing in the TV docusoap *The Cruise*.

QUIZ TEN

....

5 POINT CLUE This famous man was born in 1853, the eldest
son of a pastor. When he was 20 years of age he moved from
mainland Europe to work in London.

4 POINT CLUE Titles of his work include *Houses of Parliament*
and *Ville d'Avray*.

3 POINT CLUE In 1972 he was the subject of a No. 1 hit record
and he was played on film by Kirk Douglas in the 1950s film *Lust
For Life*.

2 POINT CLUE He was born in North Brabant in the
Netherlands and the city of Amsterdam houses a museum
dedicated to his life's work.

1 POINT CLUE This famous Dutch artist, who painted *Sunflowers*,
committed suicide.

ANSWER
VINCENT VAN GOGH

QUIZ ONE

5 POINT CLUE This famous sportsman was born on October 14th 1960 and retired in 1994.

4 POINT CLUE In 1986 he was awarded the MBE and in the previous year he broke three world records in the space of 19 days.

3 POINT CLUE In 1978 he competed in his first Commonwealth Games and five years later he won a gold medal in the World Athletic Championships.

2 POINT CLUE He was born in Gateshead and on TV he has advertised Start breakfast cereal.

1 POINT CLUE In 1984 he won an Olympic silver medal finishing second to Sebastian Coe and he shares the same initials with Seb Coe.

ANSWER
STEVE CRAM

QUIZ TWO

5 POINT CLUE This famous actor was born in 1942 and made his film debut in 1962 in *The Loneliness Of The Long Distance Runner*. An early TV appearance for this actor came in *Z Cars*.

4 POINT CLUE Other films he has appeared in include *Cry Freedom*, *Dr Phibes Rides Again*, *The Last Grenade* and *Chaplin*.

3 POINT CLUE He played a military policeman in the 1960s TV drama *Redcap* and in the 1980s he played a sitcom character called Henry Willows.

2 POINT CLUE He married the actress Sheila Hancock.

1 POINT CLUE He played the title role in *Inspector Morse*.

ANSWER
JOHN THAW

QUIZ THREE

5 POINT CLUE This famous singer was born in Texas in 1938 and whilst at school he formed his first pop group, which was called the Scholars.

4 POINT CLUE His brother Lelan worked as a promoter for Decca records and in 1958 this singer signed his first recording contract. In 1959 he joined the jazz group the Bobby Doyle Trio.

3 POINT CLUE In 1980 he starred in the film *The Gambler* and in 1977 and 1980 he topped the UK singles charts.

2 POINT CLUE In 1983 he duetted with Sheena Easton on the song 'We've Got Tonight' and in the same year he duetted with Dolly Parton on the song 'Islands In The Stream'.

1 POINT CLUE The titles of his two No. 1 hits were 'Lucille' and 'Coward Of The County'.

ANSWER
KENNY ROGERS

QUIZ FOUR

5 POINT CLUE This famous lady was born in 1933 and made her screen debut in 1952 in a film called *I Believe In You*.

4 POINT CLUE In 1979 she was voted World's Sexiest Woman and she wrote the first edition of her autobiography in 1978, which was entitled *Past Imperfect*.

3 POINT CLUE Other films include *The Virgin Queen*, *Empire Of The Ants*, *Alfie Darling* and *Road To Hong Kong*.

2 POINT CLUE In 1996 she won a court case brought against her by the publishing firm Random House, who claimed the novel she had written for a $1.3 million advance was unpublishable. She did however pen a published novel called *Prime Time* but her sister is the more famous and successful author.

1 POINT CLUE She starred on film as *The Bitch* which helped her land her famous role in the TV soap *Dynasty*.

ANSWER
JOAN COLLINS

QUIZ FIVE

....

5 POINT CLUE This mystery lady was born in 1956 and made her acting debut in a Radio 2 play about Betty Grable called *I Can't Begin To Tell You*.

4 POINT CLUE She once posed naked whilst pregnant for a controversial painting entitled *Eight Months Gone*.

3 POINT CLUE She also appeared nude on stage in the play *The Graduate* in which she replaced Kathleen Turner in the role of Mrs Robinson.

2 POINT CLUE She has appeared in a TV advert for Bovril and has appeared on the front cover of a Roxy Music album.

I POINT CLUE She described Mick Jagger as the best lover in the world.

ANSWER
JERRY HALL

QUIZ SIX

5 POINT CLUE This famous name in the world of show-business was born in January 1925 and after World War II he was signed by the theatrical agent Richard Stone to work as a straight man to Reg Varney.

4 POINT CLUE In 1991, the year prior to his death, he received the Charlie Chaplin International Award for Comedy.

3 POINT CLUE He was born in Southampton and films he has appeared in include *Chitty, Chitty, Bang, Bang, The Italian Job* and *Those Magnificent Men In Their Flying Machines.*

2 POINT CLUE In 1989 Thames TV dropped his TV show denouncing it as sexist.

I POINT CLUE He had a No. I hit with 'Ernie The Fastest Milkman In The West'.

ANSWER
BENNY HILL

QUIZ SEVEN

5 POINT CLUE This mystery man was born illegitimately in October 1913 in a small town just outside the German city of Bonn.

4 POINT CLUE As a teenager he was a member of the Hitler youth and by the time he had reached the age of 22 he applied to join the SS. In 1940 he married with a full SS guard of honour in Berlin.

3 POINT CLUE After World War II he became a successful businessman owning his own saw mill. His son died in a hang-gliding accident and his wife died of cancer.

2 POINT CLUE In 1983 he was expelled from Bolivia and extradited to France to stand trial for crimes against humanity.

1 POINT CLUE He was nicknamed the Butcher of Lyons.

ANSWER
KLAUS BARBIE

QUIZ EIGHT

5 POINT CLUE This famous man attended Newport Free Grammar School, Essex, and his first job on leaving school was as a vegetable peeler. He went on to become a top-selling author.

4 POINT CLUE Towards the end of the 20th century he formed his own pop group called Scarlet Division.

3 POINT CLUE The Chemical Brothers were flown in by helicopter to provide the music at his well-publicised showbiz marriage.

2 POINT CLUE He has been seen on a number of TV adverts including one in which he prepared a spicy prawn curry.

1 POINT CLUE He is also known as the Naked Chef.

ANSWER
JAMIE OLIVER

QUIZ NINE

5 POINT CLUE This famous lady was raised in the suburbs of Plymouth and in the year 2000 she was appointed Vice-President of the Red Cross.

4 POINT CLUE Her first job was in the photographic department of *The Western Morning News*. She eventually became a junior reporter before leaving to join the BBC in 1966.

3 POINT CLUE In 1983 she began working for *TV AM* and in an infamous incident in 1994 she poured a glass of wine over Robin Malcolm after she was sacked from a radio station.

2 POINT CLUE She hosted the TV game-show *Master Teams* and she once revealed her dancing prowess on the *Morecambe and Wise* Show.

1 POINT CLUE In 1975 she became the BBC's first female newsreader.

ANSWER
ANGELA RIPPON

QUIZ TEN

5 POINT CLUE This mystery actor was born in 1934 and he left Rokeby School in Wimbledon in 1950. After his National Service he worked as an office boy before joining RADA.

4 POINT CLUE He made his West End debut in 1958 in a stage production called *Gilt and Gingerbread*. In the same year he made his big screen debut in a film called *Girls At Sea*. Two years earlier he met his wife to be, a fellow thespian called Ann Davis.

3 POINT CLUE He was cast as Nathaniel in Kenneth Branagh's *Love's Labour's Lost* and in a later TV role he played the character of Hector McDonald in *Monarch of the Glen*.

2 POINT CLUE In the 1980s TV sitcom *Ever Decreasing Circles* he played a neurotic character called Martin.

I POINT CLUE In 1975 he successfully auditioned for a role in *The Good Life* in which Felicity Kendal played his wife.

ANSWER
RICHARD BRIERS

QUIZ ONE

5 POINT CLUE This mystery actor was born in 1949 and in 1965 he appeared as a guest trumpeter for the Syracuse Symphony Orchestra. He gave up a university scholarship to join an acting group and in 1973 he starred as Danny in a New York stage production of *Grease*.

4 POINT CLUE Following his conversion to Buddhism he set up the International Campaign for Tibet and in 1997 he brought out a book called *Pilgrim*, a book of photographs he had taken of Tibet and its surrounding countries.

3 POINT CLUE Films he has appeared in include *Rhapsody In August*, *Internal Affairs*, *King David* and *First Knight*.

2 POINT CLUE In 1995 his divorce from Cindy Crawford became absolute.

1 POINT CLUE On film he was an officer and a gentleman and he wooed a pretty woman.

ANSWER
RICHARD GERE

QUIZ TWO

5 POINT CLUE This famous British sportsman was born in 1963 and made his international debut for Scotland in 1986.

4 POINT CLUE He first played league football for St Johnstone and as an 18-year-old, he played for Sunderland FC.

3 POINT CLUE He has played and scored in several Old Firm derbies but at the end of the 20th century he was plying his trade for Kilmarnock FC.

2 POINT CLUE He has appeared in a number of TV adverts for the high street chain Farm Foods.

1 POINT CLUE He has also been seen on TV opposing John Parrott as a team captain on *A Question Of Sport*.

ANSWER
ALLY McCOIST

QUIZ THREE

5 POINT CLUE This famous lady was born in May 1970. She has worked as an ambassador for UNESCO and in 1995 she appeared in a documentary entitled *Unzipped*.

4 POINT CLUE She has posed naked for the magazines *Playboy* and *GQ*, and in the year 2000 she signed a seven-year contract to endorse Wella hair products.

3 POINT CLUE She appeared in the Michael Jackson video for the song 'In The Closet'.

2 POINT CLUE Following the break up of her relationship with Robert De Niro she became engaged to Adam Clayton of U2.

1 POINT CLUE She began her modelling career at the age of 15 and she was one of several supermodels to open the Fashion Café.

ANSWER
NAOMI CAMPBELL

QUIZ FOUR

5 POINT CLUE This famous man was born in the year that England won football's World Cup. After leaving grammar school he worked as a Tarzan-a-gram.

4 POINT CLUE As a youngster his ambition was to be a DJ and consequently he landed a job for Piccadilly Radio as an office boy. After continually badgering the management at Piccadilly, they allowed him to stand in for the resident DJs when they were on holiday.

3 POINT CLUE He also worked as the producer for a radio show hosted by Jonathan Ross, and on April 2nd 1995 he began working on Radio One's breakfast show.

2 POINT CLUE His own company is called Ginger Productions and he bought Virgin Radio from Richard Branson.

1 POINT CLUE In December 2000 it was widely reported in the tabloids that he bought the teenage singer Billie Piper a Ferrari.

ANSWER
CHRIS EVANS

QUIZ FIVE

5 POINT CLUE This famous man was born in Yorkshire in 1961. As a teenager he won a public-speaking competition organised by Yorkshire TV and he went on to attend Oxford University.

4 POINT CLUE In 1989 he won the Richmond by-election standing against Miss Whiplash and Screaming Lord Sutch.

3 POINT CLUE His middle name is Jefferson and as a 16-year-old he delivered a televised speech at the Conservative Party Conference.

2 POINT CLUE At the age of 34 he landed the post of Secretary of State for Wales in the Conservative government, which made him the youngest Cabinet Minister since Harold Wilson.

1 POINT CLUE 1997 was a defining year for this politician. He got married and became leader of the Conservative Party.

ANSWER
WILLIAM HAGUE

QUIZ SIX

5 POINT CLUE This famous actor, the son of a policeman, was born in October 1927 in London. His first Hollywood film appearance came alongside Elizabeth Taylor in a film called *The Last Time I Saw Paris*.

4 POINT CLUE He has also worked as a model and a film cartoonist. His second wife was the singer Dorothy Squires.

3 POINT CLUE His films include *Shout At The Devil*, *Gold*, *The Sea Wolves* and *The Wild Geese*.

2 POINT CLUE On TV he has played a Persuader, Ivanhoe and the Saint.

1 POINT CLUE He starred as 007 in several films, the last of which was *A View To A Kill*.

ANSWER
ROGER MOORE

4

QUIZ SEVEN

5 POINT CLUE This famous man was born in March 1879 in the German city of Ulm. From the ages of six to 15 he attended a school called the Luitpold Gymnasium.

4 POINT CLUE He worked as a clerk for the Swiss Patent Office in Berne and in 1908 he was appointed an associate professor of the University of Zurich.

3 POINT CLUE He died on April 18th 1955 and in 1981 he was the subject of a Top 10 hit record by a pop group called Landscape.

2 POINT CLUE In 1921 he was awarded the Nobel Prize for physics.

1 POINT CLUE According to his theory of relativity $E = MC^2$.

QUIZ EIGHT

5 POINT CLUE This famous man was born in 1901 and had a 25-year association with J Edgar Hoover, as a special agent whose main task was to expose communists in the world of show-business.

4 POINT CLUE He died in 1966 shortly after his 65th birthday and the first film that he made was called *Alice's Day At Sea*.

3 POINT CLUE In his lifetime he won five Emmys, the Irving Thalberg Award, the Presidential Freedom Medal, the French Legion of Honour and 31 Oscars.

2 POINT CLUE He was nicknamed Hollywood's Dark Prince and he once said 'I loved that mouse more than any woman I've ever known'.

I POINT CLUE His film studios made *Snow White And The Seven Dwarves*, the first full-length animated film.

ANSWER
WALT DISNEY

QUIZ NINE

5 POINT CLUE This mystery lady, famous in the world of show-business, left stage school to join an all girl band called Milan, who once supported East 17 on a UK concert tour.

4 POINT CLUE Her debut single as a soloist was entitled 'Are You Man Enough?', but it only crept into the lower reaches of the charts, peaking at No. 62. Her debut album was called 'You, Me and Us'.

3 POINT CLUE When she was just 23 years of age she signed a million pound record deal with Virgin Records and in 1999 she had a Top 10 hit record with a cover version of the song 'Talking In Your Sleep'.

2 POINT CLUE In 2001 she appeared in the stage production of *My Fair Lady* playing Eliza Doolittle.

1 POINT CLUE She became a household name after appearing as Tiffany in *EastEnders*.

ANSWER
MARTINE McCUTCHEON

QUIZ TEN

5 POINT CLUE This famous lady was born in 1948, brought up on a Leicester council estate and left school at the age of 14 to work in a Birds Eye factory.

4 POINT CLUE Her second husband Colin Broadway persuaded her to take up a career in writing and subsequently in 1982 BBC radio broadcast a play she had written.

3 POINT CLUE One of her novels is set just before the 1997 General Election and in 2001 it was adapted into a TV series starring Stephen Mangam in the title role.

2 POINT CLUE She wrote the best-selling novel in the UK of the 1980s, which has spawned several sequels.

1 POINT CLUE The title character of those novels is Adrian Mole.

ANSWER
SUE TOWNSEND

QUIZ ONE

5 POINT CLUE This famous man was born in 1923 and read geology at Cambridge University. He joined the RAF aged 17 after lying about his age and saw active service during World War II.

4 POINT CLUE In 2001 he was knighted in the New Year's Honours List.

3 POINT CLUE He presented the same TV programme for 44 years.

2 POINT CLUE Asteroid 2602 has been named after this famous man and he is known as an accomplished xylophone player.

1 POINT CLUE He is famous for presenting the astronomy TV series *The Sky At Night*.

ANSWER
PATRICK MOORE

QUIZ TWO

5 POINT CLUE This mystery man, famous in the world of sport, was born in February 1948 and won his first trophy as a manager in 1979.

4 POINT CLUE He is famous in the world of football and his playing career was cut short by an injury in 1975. The following year he took up his first managerial post.

3 POINT CLUE In the 20th century he managed eight different teams at club level and his trophies include a league title in 1981 and a European trophy in 1982.

2 POINT CLUE Gothenberg, Benfica and Roma are three of the clubs he has managed.

1 POINT CLUE His first match in charge of the England team resulted in a 3-0 victory over Spain.

ANSWER
SVEN GÖRAN ERIKSON

QUIZ THREE

5 POINT CLUE This famous man was born in Cheshire in 1832. He died in 1898 and during his lifetime he was a maths teacher at Oxford University.

4 POINT CLUE He was a very famous author and one of his less successful novels was entitled *Sylvie and Bruno*.

3 POINT CLUE He will definitely be remembered for one particular novel which has been filmed several times, most notably by the Disney studios.

2 POINT CLUE His real name is Charles Lutwidge Dodgson.

1 POINT CLUE He wrote of Alice's adventures In Wonderland.

ANSWER
LEWIS CARROLL

QUIZ FOUR

5 POINT CLUE This mystery actor was born in 1914 and married the ballet dancer Edna Swallow. In 1956 he began working as a continuity announcer for Granada TV.

4 POINT CLUE His first acting role came in a TV series called 'Shadow Squad'. He will however be best remembered for one particular role on TV which gained him his own appreciation society who dubbed him 'The greatest living Englishman'.

3 POINT CLUE His real surname is Popley. He appeared in 1200 episodes of one particular TV programme. His first line in the first of those episodes was 'A pint of mild and twenty fags Missus'.

2 POINT CLUE He died aged 69 in 1984, having played the same character on TV for 20 years. That character enjoyed a variety of jobs which included chauffeur, coalman, milkman, ice-cream man and window cleaner.

1 POINT CLUE He played Stan Ogden in *Coronation Street*.

ANSWER
BERNARD YOUENS

QUIZ FIVE

5 POINT CLUE This famous lady was born in March 1947 in Oxfordshire. She served in the WRAF in Singapore where she took up amateur dramatics.

4 POINT CLUE She has written several books for children and these include *The Bear Who Was Left Behind* and *Jack Crater*. In 1981 she married the theatre producer Dudley Russell.

3 POINT CLUE In 1975 she became a star after appearing on *Opportunity Knocks* which led to her own TV shows and an appearance in the 1977 Silver Jubilee Royal Variety Performance.

2 POINT CLUE In 1987 she toured the UK with her own stage show which was recorded by BBC TV and she has also been the resident humorist in the HTV programme *It's Nearly Saturday*.

1 POINT CLUE As well as writing best-selling books of poetry she released Two top 30 albums in 1976, the first of which was called 'Some Of Me Poems And Songs'.

ANSWER
PAM AYRES

QUIZ SIX

5 POINT CLUE This actor, famous on both the small and big screen, was born in 1931 and made his film debut when he was just 20 years of age in a film called *Queen For A Day*.

4 POINT CLUE Other films include *The Balcony*, *Rhubarb* and the remake of *Invasion Of The Body Snatchers*. In 1994 his voice could be heard in the animated feature *The Pagemaster*.

3 POINT CLUE His name is synonymous with one particular role, which began on TV in the 1960s and was then transferred to the big screen for a film and several sequels.

2 POINT CLUE On TV he starred as an agent in *Mission Impossible* and he directed the film *Three Men And A Baby*.

1 POINT CLUE His autobiography is entitled *I Am Not Spock*.

ANSWER
LEONARD NIMOY

QUIZ SEVEN

5 POINT CLUE This mystery man was born in London in March 1947. He started having piano lessons aged four and in 1961 he joined a rhythm and blues band called Bluesology.

4 POINT CLUE His first single as a soloist, entitled 'I've Been Loving You Too Long', failed to chart and in 1969 he released his debut album *Empty Sky*.

3 POINT CLUE He has recorded duets with George Michael, Millie Jackson, John Lennon, Aretha Franklin, Luciano Pavarotti, Eric Clapton and Marcella Detroit.

2 POINT CLUE He was born Reginald Kenneth Dwight and was the subject of a documentary called *Tantrums and Tiaras*.

1 POINT CLUE Following the death of the Princess of Wales his song 'Candle In The Wind' became the best-selling song of all time.

ANSWER
ELTON JOHN

QUIZ EIGHT

5 POINT CLUE This famous man was born in Blackburn in September 1934 and after leaving university he became an English and drama teacher.

4 POINT CLUE He began his broadcasting career in 1967 working as a producer for BBC radio. In 1969 he moved into television and three years later won the Royal Television Society Award for Most Outstanding Newcomer.

3 POINT CLUE He won an Emmy Award for his production of the TV series *Aquarius* and in addition to his broadcasting skills he penned a weekly column in the *Sunday Times*.

2 POINT CLUE In 1972 London Weekend Television gave him his own chat show and in 1988 he died from hepatitis.

I POINT CLUE On one of his chat-shows he was famously attacked by singer and model Grace Jones.

ANSWER
RUSSELL HARTY

QUIZ NINE

....

5 POINT CLUE This famous actress of stage, screen and TV was born in June 1933. She made her film debut in the 1952 film *Laxdale Hall*.

4 POINT CLUE She has appeared in numerous TV productions including *Dalziel & Pascoe*, *Begerac*, *After Henry*, *Never The Twain* and *Midsomer Murders*.

3 POINT CLUE Her films include *The Wicked Lady*, *The Boys From Brazil* and *Mad Cows* and in 1991 she played the Queen in a TV film called *A Question of Attribution*.

2 POINT CLUE She is married to the actor Timothy West and has appeared in a number of TV adverts playing the mother of Jane Horrocks.

I POINT CLUE In *Fawlty Towers* she played Sybil Fawlty.

ANSWER
PRUNELLA SCALES

QUIZ TEN

....

5 POINT CLUE This famous man was born in New York in 1899 and has been played in films many times, including portrayals by Jason Robards and Neville Brand.

4 POINT CLUE His business card read 'Second-Hand Furniture Dealer'.

3 POINT CLUE He was jailed for tax evasion in 1931 and died behind bars in 1947.

2 POINT CLUE In the film *The Untouchables* he was played by Robert De Niro.

1 POINT CLUE This gangster led the Chicago Mafia and was nicknamed Scarface.

ANSWER
AL CAPONE

QUIZ ONE

5 POINT CLUE This famous actor was born in 1925 and made his film debut in 1948 in *The Last Days Of Dolwyn*. The subtitle of a 1986 biography of his life was *The Man Behind The Myth*.

4 POINT CLUE Although he was nominated seven times for Oscars he never actually received an Academy Award. He was first nominated in 1952 for the film *My Cousin Rachel*.

3 POINT CLUE He once said 'When I played drunks I had to remain sober because I didn't know how to play them when I was drunk'.

2 POINT CLUE He died in 1984 and coincidentally *1984* was the title of his final film appearance on the big screen.

1 POINT CLUE He married Elizabeth Taylor on two occasions.

ANSWER
RICHARD BURTON

QUIZ TWO

5 POINT CLUE This man, a famous name in the world of football, was born in 1960 and made his Football League debut in 1978. He won his first cap for England when he was 26 years old.

4 POINT CLUE He was voted Footballer of the Year in 1986 and 1992 and he has played league football in England, Spain and Japan.

3 POINT CLUE In 1986 he won the World Cup's Golden Boot Award and only Bobby Charlton has scored more goals for England than this man.

2 POINT CLUE In 1995 he was made a Freeman of the city of Leicester. Since his retirement he has moved into the world of broadcasting including hosting *Grandstand*.

1 POINT CLUE He is also a team captain on the game-show *They Think It's All Over* and can be seen in various disguises for Walker's crisps TV adverts.

ANSWER
GARY LINEKER

QUIZ THREE

5 POINT CLUE This famous singer was born in New York in 1941. He dropped out of New York University in 1962 to take a job as an apprentice song writer for Sunbeam Music, which earned him $50 a week.

4 POINT CLUE Before hitting the big time as a singer in his own right, he wrote numerous hits for other artists including Cliff Richard, Bobby Vinton and Jimmy Clanton.

3 POINT CLUE He wrote the songs 'Red, Red Wine' and 'I'm A Believer'. The first major hit that he himself sang was entitled 'Cherry, Cherry' a Top 10 hit in the USA.

2 POINT CLUE His real name is Noah Kaminsky and he played the title role in the film remake of *The Jazz Singer*.

1 POINT CLUE His biggest hits include 'Forever In Blue Jeans', 'Cracklin' Rosie' and 'Sweet Caroline'.

ANSWER
NEIL DIAMOND

QUIZ FOUR

5 POINT CLUE This mystery man was born on a council estate in Dudley but went on to become a familiar face on British TV. As a teenager he joined the Max Roberts acting group in the mining village of Blackworth.

4 POINT CLUE He founded his own TV production company called Coastal and he co-starred alongside Tara Fitzgerald in the drama *The Student Prince*.

3 POINT CLUE In 1995 he featured on an album, sales of which grossed over £50 million world wide. He has sung on No. 1 hits which were all cover versions.

2 POINT CLUE His first big break on TV came when he landed the role of a hospital porter called Jimmy in *Casualty*.

1 POINT CLUE He co-starred with Jerome Flynn in *Soldier, Soldier* and duetted with him on his No. 1 hits.

ANSWER
ROBSON GREEN

6

QUIZ FIVE

5 POINT CLUE This famous lady was born in 1946 and her 1989 autobiography is entitled *Stare Back and Smile*. As a teenager she worked at a Debenham's store for £8 per week, before realising her ambition to become an actress. In 1968 she appeared in her first film which was called *Some Girls Do*.

4 POINT CLUE In the film *Parting Shots* she played a brassy barmaid and in the film *James And The Giant Peach* she played a wicked spinster.

3 POINT CLUE On TV her co-stars have included David McCallum, June Whitfield and Gareth Hunt.

2 POINT CLUE She played a prostitute in the film *Shirley Valentine* and on TV she played the title role in *Willoughby MD*.

1 POINT CLUE She sprang to fame as Purdey in *The New Avengers* and won a BAFTA Award for her role in *Absolutely Fabulous*.

ANSWER
JOANNA LUMLEY

QUIZ SIX

5 POINT CLUE This mystery sportsman was born in February 1950 and during his career he broke 32 world records.

4 POINT CLUE After retiring from competition he worked for the ABC Sports Network and appeared in a variety of adverts endorsing numerous hair and skin products.

3 POINT CLUE He was born in California and in 1972 he was named World Athlete of the Year.

2 POINT CLUE He had amassed 17 national records by the age of 10 and eight years later he competed in his first Olympics. He won two gold medals at that Olympics, both for the relay.

1 POINT CLUE This famous American swimmer won seven gold medals at the 1972 Munich Olympics.

ANSWER
MARK SPITZ

QUIZ SEVEN

5 POINT CLUE This famous man was born in London in 1930. He worked as a call boy at the Lewisham Hippodrome where he also operated the spotlight. During his time there he was taught to play the ukelele by the legendary George Formby.

4 POINT CLUE On TV he has hosted the quiz shows *It's Your Word* and *Three Little Words* and he also wrote 26 episodes of the sitcom *Bootsie And Snudge*.

3 POINT CLUE He created and appeared in the children's TV series *Tich And Quackers*.

2 POINT CLUE He has written a book entitled *Gottle Of Geer*.

I POINT CLUE He is one of Britain's most famous ventriloquists and his most famous doll is called Lord Charles.

QUIZ EIGHT

5 POINT CLUE This famous lady was born in New Jersey in 1963 and began her singing career, aged eight, with the New Hope Baptist Junior Choir. Within four years she was singing backing vocals for such artists as Chaka Khan and Lou Rawls.

4 POINT CLUE Her first single 'You Give Good Love' failed to chart in Britain but was a No. 3 hit in the USA. Since then her world-wide album sales have exceeded 100 million.

3 POINT CLUE She has duetted with Teddy Pendergrass, Aretha Franklin and Mariah Carey and in 1992 she recorded the best-selling song ever by a female artist.

2 POINT CLUE Her first chart-topping single was entitled 'Saving All My Love For You' a song she could possibly have serenaded her husband Bobby Brown with.

I POINT CLUE She co-starred in the film *The Bodyguard* with Kevin Costner.

ANSWER
WHITNEY HOUSTON

6

QUIZ NINE

5 POINT CLUE This famous man was born in Milwaukee in 1919, the son of a penniless Italian immigrant. When he was just nine years old he played with the Chicago Symphony Orchestra.

4 POINT CLUE He appeared in a handful of films including a 1949 production called *East Of Java* in which he played a pianist. Early in his career he performed under the name of Walter Busterkeys.

3 POINT CLUE At the 1978 Royal Variety Performance he appeared in a replica of George V's coronation robes. He died in February 1987.

2 POINT CLUE Despite his fame he was plagued by sexual scandals and in 1959 he successfully sued a *Daily Mirror* columnist who wrote a piece questioning his sexuality.

1 POINT CLUE He was known as 'Mr Showmanship' and was renowned for his glittering costumes, extravagant jewellery and piano-shaped swimming pool.

ANSWER
LIBERACE

QUIZ TEN

5 POINT CLUE This mystery man, famous in the world of comedy, was born in Bedford in 1929. He left his job as a bank clerk and made his London stage debut in the play *Mourning Becomes Electra*.

4 POINT CLUE He appeared in his first film in 1953 which was entitled *The Silent Witness*. Other films include *A Ghost Of A Chance* and *The Magnificent Seven Deadly Sins*.

3 POINT CLUE In 1988 he starred in a short-lived TV sitcom called *Clarence* in which he played a short-sighted removal man.

2 POINT CLUE In 1966 he joined the cast of *The Frost Report* which was to prove a turning point in his career. It was here that he met a fellow comedian who became his working partner in a TV comedy series that ran for 17 years.

1 POINT CLUE He starred as Arkwright in *Open All Hours* and as Fletcher in *Porridge*.

ANSWER
RONNIE BARKER

QUIZ ONE

5 POINT CLUE This mystery man, famous in the world of sport, was born in 1964 and made his Olympic debut in 1984.

4 POINT CLUE He won a gold medal at the 1986 Commonwealth Games and followed that with an Olympic gold two years later.

3 POINT CLUE His middle name is Claudius and in 1989 he made his professional debut at the Albert Hall.

2 POINT CLUE The only defeat in his professional career in the 20th century was inflicted by Oliver McCall.

1 POINT CLUE He represented Canada at the Olympics, but fighting under the British flag he defeated Evander Holyfield to become the Boxing Heavyweight Champion of the World.

ANSWER
LENNOX LEWIS

QUIZ TWO

5 POINT CLUE This famous actor was born in 1952 and his voice could be heard in the animated feature *Fern Gully The Last Rain Forest*. Prior to his acting career he was a night club comedian.

4 POINT CLUE He once said, "Cocaine is God's way of saying you're making too much money".

3 POINT CLUE His less successful films include *Club Paradise*, *Being Human* and *The Adventures of Baron Munchausen*.

2 POINT CLUE He won an Academy Award for his role in the 1997 film *Good Will Hunting*.

1 POINT CLUE On film he has played Popeye and Mrs Doubtfire.

ANSWER
ROBIN WILLIAMS

QUIZ THREE

5 POINT CLUE This mystery man was born in April 1938 and on leaving school worked as a junior clerk for the Eston Urban Council. Early in his showbiz career he was one half of a double act called the Eldanis.

4 POINT CLUE In 1985 his TV series won a Golden Rose at the Montreux TV Festival and one of his sons has served a jail sentence for fraud.

3 POINT CLUE He came second in the talent show *Opportunity Knocks* and his autobiography is entitled *Under No Illusion*.

2 POINT CLUE He hosted the game shows *Odd One Out* and *Every Second Counts* and he married his assistant Debbie McGee.

1 POINT CLUE His car bears the registration plate MAG 1C and his double act the Eldanis is an anagram of his surname.

ANSWER
PAUL DANIELS

QUIZ FOUR

5 POINT CLUE This mystery actress was born in July 1928 and appeared in the films *The Dresser* and *Mary Reilly*.

4 POINT CLUE In 1969 she starred in a short-lived soap opera called *Castle Haven* in which she played a character called Lorna Everett. In that soap Roy Barrowclough played her husband.

3 POINT CLUE She also played Vera Hopkins in *Coronation Street* and Mrs Blewitt in *Open All Hours*.

2 POINT CLUE For many years she played the character of Doris Luke in *Crossroads*, a role that was reprised in the return of *Crossroads* in 2001.

1 POINT CLUE She became a national institution for her role as Nora Batty in *Last of the Summer Wine*.

7

QUIZ FIVE

5 POINT CLUE This famous actor was born in 1954 and first came to our attention in the lead role of a Broadway stage play called *When Chickens Come Home To Roost*.

4 POINT CLUE He was one of the many stars of the US Civil War film *Glory* and he co-starred with Whitney Houston in the film *The Bishop's Wife*.

3 POINT CLUE He became a big star in the USA after playing a doctor in the Emmy Award-winning TV series *St Elsewhere*.

2 POINT CLUE He shares his surname with that of an American city.

1 POINT CLUE He received much critical acclaim for his film portrayal of *Malcolm X*.

ANSWER
DENZEL WASHINGTON

70

QUIZ SIX

5 POINT CLUE This mystery sportsman was born in October 1960 and made his international debut aged 17. He scored his first international goal two years later against Scotland.

4 POINT CLUE In 1989 he won the UEFA Cup Winner's Medal.

3 POINT CLUE In 1982 he signed for Barcelona before leaving two years later to join an Italian club.

2 POINT CLUE A former World Footballer of the Year, he was born in a suburb of Buenos Aires.

1 POINT CLUE In 1986 he scored the infamous 'Hand of God' goal against England.

ANSWER
DIEGO MARADONA

QUIZ SEVEN

5 POINT CLUE This mystery lady was born in 1650 in Pipe Well Lane in Hereford. One of her children became the Duke of St Albans.

4 POINT CLUE Her life story was told in a 1934 film starring Cedric Hardwicke and Anna Neagle. She died in 1687 and was buried in the church grounds of St Martin in the Fields in London.

3 POINT CLUE At the age of 15 she was given her first stage part in a play by John Dryden called *Indian Emperor*. More parts followed specially written for her by Dryden and she was soon accepted as an outstanding comedienne.

2 POINT CLUE Samuel Pepys described her in his diaries as 'A bold and merry slut'.

1 POINT CLUE She rose from selling oranges in Drury Lane to become the favourite mistress of Charles II.

ANSWER
NELL GWYN

QUIZ EIGHT

5 POINT CLUE This mystery man was born in October 1928 in Lincolnshire. After leaving Glasgow University he gave his first radio broadcast in *The Radio Deceiver*.

4 POINT CLUE He has appeared on stage in a number of Brian Rix farces and made his film debut at the age of 19 in *Master Of Bankdom*.

3 POINT CLUE Although he will not be best remembered as a film star he has appeared in 16 films, including *Doctor In Love* and *Carry On Regardless*.

2 POINT CLUE Early in his showbiz career he played the straight man to the comedians Arthur Haynes and Benny Hill.

1 POINT CLUE During the 1970s he was the host of the quiz show *The Sale Of The Century*.

ANSWER
NICHOLAS PARSONS

QUIZ NINE

5 POINT CLUE This mystery actress was born in Scotland in 1934. She trained at the Bristol Old Vic, Theatre School and made her big screen debut in the 1965 film *Sky West And Crooked*.

4 POINT CLUE Other films include *Hawk The Slayer*, *The Slipper And The Rose* and *The Pope Must Die*.

3 POINT CLUE On TV she has starred in many dramas including *Lily Langtry*, *An Unsuitable Job For A Woman* and *Taggart*.

2 POINT CLUE In the TV dramas *Edward VII* and *The Six Wives Of Henry VIII* she played Queen Victoria and Catherine of Aragon.

I POINT CLUE She will probably be best remembered for her role as the long-suffering wife of Victor Meldrew.

ANSWER
ANNETTE CROSBIE

QUIZ TEN

5 POINT CLUE This mystery man, famous in the world of pop music, was born in New York in March 1942 and early in his career he played in a group called the Shades.

4 POINT CLUE In 1987 he collaborated with Sam Moore on a reworking of Sam & Dave's 'Soul Man' which was used as the theme music to the film of the same name. In 1974 he had a Top 10 album in the USA entitled 'Sally Can't Dance'.

3 POINT CLUE In 1989 he wrote and composed a 50-minute piece called 'Songs For Drella. A Fiction', which was a tribute to Andy Warhol.

2 POINT CLUE His real name is Louis Firbank and he was a founder member of the cult group Velvet Underground.

1 POINT CLUE He wrote the song 'Perfect Day' and featured on its charity re-release with a host of other stars.

ANSWER
LOU REED

QUIZ ONE

5 POINT CLUE This mystery man, an icon in the world of show-business, was born in the East End of London in October 1922. Early in his career he toured the capital and billed himself as 'The Lazy Comic'.

4 POINT CLUE His first film role came in 1949 in *Skimpy In The Navy* and his first hit record was entitled 'Cowpuncher's Cantata', which reached the Top 20 in 1952.

3 POINT CLUE In the 20th century he appeared in a record 19 Royal Variety Performances and he also received three platinum discs, 31 gold discs and 15 silver discs for his various recordings.

2 POINT CLUE He replaced Bob Monkhouse as the host of the game show *Family Fortunes*.

1 POINT CLUE His catchphrase 'I wanna tell you a story' provided the title of his autobiography.

ANSWER
MAX BYGRAVES

QUIZ TWO

5 POINT CLUE This mystery man was born in 1807, and when he died in 1882 he was mourned throughout Europe as a man who had given his life to the cause of liberty.

4 POINT CLUE In 1834 he was forced to flee to South America where he volunteered to fight for the province of Rio Grande against the Brazilian Empire.

3 POINT CLUE In 1848 he returned to his homeland where he commanded troops defending the Roman Republic against the French.

2 POINT CLUE In 1860 he sailed from Genoa with a band of 1,000 men who were nicknamed 'The Redshirts'.

1 POINT CLUE This Italian patriot and soldier gave his name to a type of biscuit.

ANSWER
GIUSEPPE GARIBALDI

QUIZ THREE

5 POINT CLUE This famous singer was born in 1948, one of 12 children, and had 15 Top 30 hits in the 1980s including four No. 1s.

4 POINT CLUE He was born in Wales and early in his career he was backed by a band called the Sunsets.

3 POINT CLUE In 1977 he played Elvis in a London stage production of the same name. His chart debut arrived in 1980 with a song called 'Hot Dog'.

2 POINT CLUE He had his first No. 1 hit in 1981, which was a cover version of a 1954 hit for Rosemary Clooney. His real name is Michael Barrett.

1 POINT CLUE He topped the UK singles charts with the songs 'This Ole House' and 'Green Door'.

ANSWER
SHAKIN' STEVENS

QUIZ FOUR

5 POINT CLUE This mystery man, famous in the world of music, was born in 1957, raised in Brighton and suffers from an unusual allergy to feathers.

4 POINT CLUE In 1985 he won the prestigious Gramophone Award and his father was the principal cellist in the Royal Philharmonic Orchestra.

3 POINT CLUE He is one of Aston Villa FC's most famous celebrity football fans.

2 POINT CLUE From the age of seven he boarded at the Yehudi Menuhin Music School in Surrey.

1 POINT CLUE His performance of Vivaldi's *Four Seasons* became the best-selling classical album of all time.

ANSWER
NIGEL KENNEDY

QUIZ FIVE

5 POINT CLUE This famous actress was born in 1937 and when she was just 15 years old she appeared in the stage musical '*Love From Judy*' alongside June Whitfield.

4 POINT CLUE In the 1950s she appeared on film as a St Trinians schoolgirl and in the 1990s she appeared on stage with Vanessa Redgrave in *The Threepenny Opera*.

3 POINT CLUE In the children's TV series *Worzel Gummidge* she played the role of Saucy Nancy.

2 POINT CLUE The first of a number of *Carry On* films she appeared in was *Carry On Spying*.

1 POINT CLUE Her career was revitalised when she landed the role of Peggy Mitchell in *EastEnders*.

ANSWER
BARBARA WINDSOR

QUIZ SIX

5 POINT CLUE This famous singer was born in 1945 and the first single that he released was entitled 'Judge Not (Unless You Judge Yourself)'. It failed to chart in the UK, but was a smash hit in his home country.

4 POINT CLUE His hit albums include *Catch A Fire*, *Confrontation* and *Legend*.

3 POINT CLUE He died in May 1981 aged 36, and two years later had a posthumous hit with 'Buffalo Soldier'.

2 POINT CLUE He was born in Jamaica and in 1982 became the subject of a Jamaican commemorative stamp.

1 POINT CLUE He was probably the most famous reggae artist of all time and he was backed by the Wailers.

ANSWER
BOB MARLEY

QUIZ SEVEN

5 POINT CLUE This mystery lady was born in Yorkshire in 1903 and was married twice but had no children. She graduated as a Bachelor of Arts from Sheffield University.

4 POINT CLUE In 1930 she was presented with a CBE and in the same year received a £10,000 cheque from the *Daily Mail* newspaper.

3 POINT CLUE In 1929 she bought a second-hand De Havilland Moth for £600.

2 POINT CLUE It is believed that she died in 1941, although her body was never found.

1 POINT CLUE In a plane called *Jason* she became the first woman to fly solo to Australia.

ANSWER
AMY JOHNSON

QUIZ EIGHT

5 POINT CLUE This famous singer was born in 1971 and early in his career he played a singing bartender in the American soap opera *General Hospital*.

4 POINT CLUE Between the ages of 12 and 17 he performed in a boy band called Menudo.

3 POINT CLUE His hit singles include 'Shake Your Bon-Bon' and 'The Cup Of Life'. In 1998 he released the best-selling single in the history of Columbia Records.

2 POINT CLUE His real name is Enrique José Martin Morales and he was born in Puerto Rico.

1 POINT CLUE This famous singer was 'Living La Vida Loca'.

QUIZ NINE

5 POINT CLUE This mystery sportsman was born in Ohio in 1940 and turned professional when he was 21 years of age.

4 POINT CLUE He won his first amateur national championship in 1959 and three years later he won his first of many professional championships.

3 POINT CLUE Between 1964 and 1978 he was a winner or runner-up at least once a year in a golf Major.

2 POINT CLUE In 1983 he was named captain of the American Ryder Cup team.

1 POINT CLUE He was the most successful golfer of the 20th century and he was nicknamed 'The Golden Bear'.

ANSWER
JACK NICKLAUS

QUIZ TEN

5 POINT CLUE This famous actress, in accordance with her final wishes for a fun funeral, made her last entrance with a jazz band playing 'When The Saints Go Marching In'.

4 POINT CLUE As a child she featured on the radio show *Children's Hour* and when she was 35 years old she made a rare film appearance in *Blood Of The Vampire*.

3 POINT CLUE She has written scripts for Harry Worth, appeared in a seaside summer season with Thora Hird and apparently she owned a kidney-shaped swimming pool.

2 POINT CLUE Her third husband, a fellow thespian, is related to Tony Blair.

I POINT CLUE She played Elsie Tanner in *Coronation Street*.

ANSWER
PAT PHOENIX

QUIZ ONE

....

5 POINT CLUE This mystery lady, a famous singer, was born in Tennessee in November 1939, and over the years she has performed duets with Bryan Adams, Eric Clapton and Barry White.

4 POINT CLUE In 1990 she became the first woman to perform at the Palace of Versailles. She celebrated her 50th birthday as her album *Foreign Affair* entered the UK album charts at No. 1.

3 POINT CLUE Films she has appeared in include *Tommy* and *Mad Max 3: Beyond Thunderdome*.

2 POINT CLUE The story of her tempestuous marriage was chronicled in the film *What's Love Got To Do With it?*

1 POINT CLUE The boxer Chris Eubank made his ring entrances to the strains of her song 'Simply The Best'.

ANSWER
TINA TURNER

QUIZ TWO

5 POINT CLUE This mystery actor was born in Kent in September 1916, and won a scholarship to RADA in 1933. He made his professional acting debut after winning a BBC acting competition.

4 POINT CLUE He appeared in 90 films in total and in several TV productions including an Emmy-winning performance in the American production of *The Invincible Mr Disraeli*.

3 POINT CLUE He died in 1988 from influenza and bronchitis and had been married to the actress Helen Cherry since 1944.

2 POINT CLUE His films include *Cockleshell Heroes*, *Mutiny On The Bounty*, *Superman*, *Ryan's Daughter*, *Around The World In Eighty Days* and *The Charge Of The Light Brigade*.

1 POINT CLUE In 1946 he gave a memorable performance as a doctor embroiled in a hesitant love affair in the film *Brief Encounter*.

ANSWER
TREVOR HOWARD

QUIZ THREE

5 POINT CLUE This famous singer was born in 1940 and made his TV debut on the Billy Cotton Band Show.

4 POINT CLUE In the 1980s he co-wrote and starred in a stage musical called *Matador*.

3 POINT CLUE He was born with the surname of Woodward, but took his stage name from the title of a 1963 Oscar-winning film.

2 POINT CLUE He played himself in the film *Mars Attacks* and in 1999 he won a new generation of fans with his chart-topping album *Reloaded*.

1 POINT CLUE His debut single 'It's Not Unusual' was the first of several No. 1 hits for this hip-thrusting singer.

ANSWER
TOM JONES

QUIZ FOUR

5 POINT CLUE This mystery man, famous in the world of show-business, was born in 1921, and saw active service during World War II while serving in the Territorial Army. He was demobbed in 1946 and made his professional stage debut at the Windmill Theatre.

4 POINT CLUE In 1957 he made his big-screen debut in a film called *Davy*. Other films include *The Song Of Norway* and *Sunstruck*.

3 POINT CLUE In the 1980s he wrote a highly praised novel called *Twice Brightly* and this knighted entertainer died in April 2001.

2 POINT CLUE On TV he presented the religious programme *Highway* and he was one of the many stars of the musical *Oliver*.

I POINT CLUE This famous Welshman was a member of the Goons.

ANSWER
SIR HARRY SECOMBE

9

QUIZ FIVE

5 POINT CLUE This famous American was born in 1848 and died in 1928. A 1997 biography about his life was sub-titled *The Life Behind The Legend*.

4 POINT CLUE He was played many times on film, the first of which came in 1931 when the actor George O'Brien played him.

3 POINT CLUE Other actors to have played him on film include Walter Huston, Randolph Scott, Henry Fonda, James Stewart and Kevin Costner.

2 POINT CLUE He was played in a long-running TV series by Hugh O'Brian and he was also played by Kurt Russell in the film *Tombstone*.

1 POINT CLUE This famous American lawman of the Wild West fought in the gunfight at the OK Corral alongside his brothers and Doc Holliday.

ANSWER
WYATT EARP

90

QUIZ SIX

5 POINT CLUE This famous actor, a familiar face on British TV, was born in 1962 and early in his acting career starred in the TV programmes *Anne of Avonlea* and *The Tomorrow People*.

4 POINT CLUE In the year 2001 he played a character called Dr Moss and in the previous year he played the Dickens character Uriah Heep in a lavish TV production of *David Copperfield*.

3 POINT CLUE Over the years he has starred in a number of sitcoms. He played the son of Ronnie Barker in *Going Straight* and Wendy Craig's son in *Butterflies*.

2 POINT CLUE He played a number of roles in an award-winning series of TV adverts for WH Smith.

1 POINT CLUE He plays Rodney Trotter in *Only Fools and Horses*.

ANSWER
NICHOLAS LYNDHURST

QUIZ SEVEN

5 POINT CLUE This famous man was born in 1929 and at the age of 15 he attended college on a special programme for gifted students. After graduating he became a pastor in Montgomery.

4 POINT CLUE In the 1960s he became the youngest ever man to win a Nobel Peace Prize.

2 POINT CLUE His all too short life was chronicled in a biography written by the politician Jesse Jackson and he was assassinated in Memphis when he was 39 years old.

2 POINT CLUE According to a TV advert this famous man is the person that footballer Ian Wright would most like to have a 'One to One' with.

1 POINT CLUE This black civil rights leader once gave a stirring speech that began with the words "I have a dream...".

ANSWER
MARTIN LUTHER KING

QUIZ EIGHT

4 POINT CLUE This famous lady was born in 1966 and made her TV debut in 1977 in the American sitcom *Good Times*. She went on to appear in a TV series called *A New Kind Of Family*.

2 POINT CLUE She played a student in the TV series *Fame* and in 1990 she received a star on Hollywood's Walk of Fame.

3 POINT CLUE In 1984 she eloped with and married James De Barge but this marriage was annulled seven months later.

2 POINT CLUE Her hit records include 'The Best Things In Life Are Free', 'That's The Way Love Goes' and 'What Have You Done For Me Lately' .

1 POINT CLUE In 1995 she duetted with her brother Michael on the song 'Scream'.

ANSWER
JANET JACKSON

QUIZ NINE

2 POINT CLUE This famous man was born in 1725, the result of an adulterous liaison between an actress and a theatre-owner. He died in 1798.

4 POINT CLUE He has been played several time on film, including portrayals by Tony Curtis, Vincent Price and Donald Sutherland.

3 POINT CLUE He was born in Venice and had many contrasting occupations during his lifetime, such as a librarian and a government spy, and he was once jailed for sorcery.

2 POINT CLUE His first name is Giovanni but he is usually referred to by his surname. In an award-winning TV drama he was played by Frank Finlay.

1 POINT CLUE He was known as the world's greatest lover.

ANSWER
CASANOVA

QUIZ TEN

5 POINT CLUE This famous actress was born on Christmas Day 1923 in London and made her TV debut as an Irish maid called Nora in *Ah Wilderness*. She made her big-screen debut in the 1945 musical *The Lisbon Story*.

4 POINT CLUE The television pioneer John Logie Baird chose her to take part in his first colour TV experiment, in which she was seen sitting on a chair trying on a variety of coloured hats.

3 POINT CLUE She died in April 1985 and although she never married she had a 20-year relationship with the showbiz impresario Val Parnell.

2 POINT CLUE She played the same role on TV for 17 years which encompassed 3,521 episodes and culminated with her waving goodbye from the deck of the *QE2*.

1 POINT CLUE She played the Crossroads Motel owner Meg Richardson.

ANSWER
NOELE GORDON